Modern C
Of Mice and Men

Mike Gould

Folens
Publishers

Acknowledgements

Folens allows photocopying of pages marked 'copiable page' for educational use, providing that this use is within the confines of the purchasing institution. Copiable pages should not be declared in any return in respect of any photocopying licence.

Editor: Hayley Willer
Illustrations: Tony O'Donnell
Cover design: Ed Gallagher

Layout artist: Louise Pellowe
Cover image: Of Mice and Men © 1992 Metro-Goldwyn-Mayer Inc
All Rights Reserved. MGM CLIP+STILL.

Of Mice and Men by John Steinbeck, published by William Heinemann: Extracts reproduced by permission of the publishers, Random House.

© 1999 Folens Limited, on behalf of the author.
Every effort has been made to contact copyright holders of material used in this book. If any have been overlooked, we will be pleased to make any necessary arrangements.

First published 1999 by Folens Limited, Dunstable and Dublin.
Folens Limited, Albert House, Apex Business Centre, Boscombe Road, Dunstable, LU5 4RL, United Kingdom.

ISBN 1 86202 646–7

Printed in Singapore by Craft Print.

Contents

Teachers' notes

Most extracts from the novel are referred to by chapter number. However, where textual page numbers are given, they refer to the Heinemann New Windmills publication of *Of Mice and Men* (1965.)

Background

The whole story (Page 6)
This activity sheet is designed to enable students to get the events (and the sequence in which they occur) clear in their minds so that recalling names and key events is not a barrier to critical analysis. The events can be cut out and rearranged if desired.

Who's who? (Page 7)
This sheet is for students' reference when writing extended assignments or when revising for an exam.

Geography and biography (Page 8)
John Steinbeck writes about places and people he knew well. It is worth pointing out to students, however, that this feature in his writing does not, in itself, make the novel realistic.

The Great Depression (Page 9)
John Steinbeck had a keen eye for the social conditions at the time the novel was conceived, and whilst *Of Mice and Men* does not depend on great social upheaval, as *The Grapes of Wrath* does, it helps explain the dreams of Lennie, George and Candy. The idea of homely aspirations, shattered by social forces, events or human weakness, is a theme picked up by Steinbeck's other novels. Students should be encouraged to research the answer to Question 5 by looking through a biographical encyclopedia or English Literature encyclopedia.

Who says? (Page 10)
Students are asked to use knowledge they have gained about characters to work out who is speaking.

First pages (Page 11)
The opening five or six pages of a novel can tell us a great deal about the story as a whole. This sheet provides some details about the opening, and then asks students to find evidence to support the statements.

A tell-tale title (Page 12)
It is generally known that the title, *Of Mice and Men*, is taken from Robert Burns' poem 'To a Mouse'. The sheet asks students to consider its relevance to the text as a whole.

What happens

Chapter 1 (Page 13)
This is essentially a recall-exercise, particularly appropriate for weaker students who can use the pictures as a prompt.

Chapter 2 (Page 14)
This sheet is in the form of a general quiz on events, and things that are said. Students should fill in answers on the sheet to use for later reference.

Chapter 3 (Page 15)
Students are presented with a cloze exercise. Common sense and context will enable most spaces to be completed, but some rereading of the Chapter is also necessary.

Chapter 4 (Page 16)
Chapter 4 consists, in the main, of four conversations. Students are asked to paraphrase and summarise the content of these conversations having been given an opening sentence to get them started.

Chapter 5 (Page 17)
This is a visual sequencing exercise. Students should place the events depicted in the correct order of occurrence and then, using the information, write a fuller summary of what happens.

Chapter 6 (Page 18)
This sheet requires some comprehension and analysis; students will need to reread the Chapter before answering the three questions based on it.

Characters

George, Lennie, Slim, Candy, Curley, Curley's Wife, Crooks (Pages 19–25)
Seven sheets, on the major characters are provided. What constitutes a major character is debatable. Carlson and Whit both say more than Curley in the story, but their roles are secondary to the main thrust of the action. These sheets should be filled in with guidance from the teacher and can be used to support essay assignments.

Minor characters (Pages 26)
Carlson, Whit and the ranch boss appear on this sheet. Aunt Clara might qualify as a minor character, but if students point this out, it is worth stating that she appears only in retrospect, or as a figment of Lennie's tortured imagination in Chapter 6.

The author

Steinbeck's language – dialect (Page 27)
This sheet ensures that students are able to follow the sense of what is being said in the novel, and also, as a by-product, revise some quotations.

Steinbeck's language – character (Page 28)
This sheet requires students to analyse details of language, use of verbs, and the way Steinbeck talks about Lennie specifically.

Teachers' notes

Steinbeck at the movies (Page 29)

Increasingly, videos are used to support the teaching of texts in class, although, as the sheet points out, *Of Mice and Men* is a relatively clear tale.

Character evaluation and relationships

Lennie's dream (Page 30)

The dream of the farm and Lennie's rabbits is central to the story. It is remarkably detailed and students should be able to extract a good deal of information from it.

Friendship (Page 31)

The nature of the relationship between Lennie and George is also central to the novel. Students are asked to explore it and try to understand why George stays with Lennie.

Motives, Questions (Pages 32–33)

Both sheets require students to take on roles, as key characters within the story and subsequently as an outsider trying to analyse the behaviour of the prime movers in the narrative.

Incident in Weed (Page 34)

Students are asked to make a creative response to the incident that occurs before the novel begins, and in so doing, use loaded language to change the focus of a newspaper story.

A marriage made in hell (Page 35)

This demands a creative response, asking students to script a conversation between Curley and his wife as a way of demonstrating their knowledge of character and language.

Mental handicap (Page 36)

It is clear that Lennie is slow-witted, but no coherent explanation is given in the novel. The explanation given by George that he was kicked in the head by a horse is almost immediately retracted. This sheet asks students to consider the extent to which Lennie is responsible for his actions, and may open up contemporary issues, such as care in the community.

The issue of race (Page 37)

In one sense, racism and the stigma of slavery are not central to the narrative of the novel, but in another sense Steinbeck's view of the noble dignity of Crooks places characters such as Curley and Carlson in sharp relief. Terms such as 'nigger' and 'coloured' are used freely throughout the novel, but it is worth pointing out that Steinbeck was reflecting a reality of the time, not condoning it.

Essay practice

Using quotations (Page 38)

This sheet provides clear advice on two ways of using quotations and gives a task so that students can practise what they have learned.

Curley's wife (Page 39)

This sheet takes students through the stages required to make a judgement about Curley's wife's character.

Tragedy revealed (Page 40)

Students are asked to think about how the notion of tragedy applies to George and Lennie. They are required to find appropriate quotations to support their ideas.

A modern-day fable (Page 41)

The idea of the novel as a 'modern fable' is considered here with analysis of the clarity and straightforward nature of the narrative. The questions posed in Stage 2 are quite challenging. The students should deduce that the story is told in chronological sequence (each chapter follows the next in order of time), the majority of the story takes place in the bunk-house, in just a few rooms (almost like a play set), and there are a limited number of characters 'there are no references to passers-by'. Students should consider whether there is a lesson learned as in a fable. (The lesson George learns is not that of someone who reforms his or her behaviour, but of someone who learns that the world is an awful place.)

The death of Candy's dog (Pages 42–43)

Students are asked to consider the elements in Steinbeck's writing that contribute to the palpable tension in the passage quoted.

Examination passages

Exam passage 1 (Pages 44–45)

Some terminal exams ask pupils to answer specific questions on a lengthy extract. This is essentially a specimen paper for students to use for practice.

Exam passage 2 (Pages 46–47)

The ending of the story is provided as a specimen paper on language, mood and tone.

Answers

Selected answers (Page 48)

This page provides answers relating to, **'The whole Story'** (Page 6), **'Who says?'** (Page 10), **'Chapter 2'** (Page 14), **'Chapter 3'** (Page 15), **'Chapter 5'** (Page 17), **'Friendship'** (Page 31)

The whole story

- To revise the order of events in the story.

1. Read this selection of the main events from *Of Mice and Men*.

a. Candy's dog is shot by Carlson.

b. Lennie accidentally kills the puppy given to him by Slim.

c. George and Lennie leave Weed after Lennie is accused (wrongly) of assaulting a local girl.

d. Lennie and George start jobs on the ranch.

e. Lennie runs off and hides in the brush by the river, waiting for George.

f. Slim gives Lennie a puppy from his own dog's litter.

g. Lennie crushes Curley's hand in a fight.

h. George shoots Lennie to stop him being locked up, or being lynched by Curley.

i. Lennie kills Curley's wife after she talks to him in the barn.

j. The boss' son, Curley, takes a dislike to Lennie and George and is distrustful of his young wife.

2. On your own, arrange these events in the correct order.

3. Compare your list with a friend's and agree the order.

4. Once you are sure the order is correct, take it in turns to tell each other the story, filling in other details where appropriate – without using the list if possible – until you have memorised it as well as you can.

MODERN CLASSICS: *Of Mice and Men*

Who's who?

FOCUS

- To become familiar with the characters from *Of Mice and Men*, and explore your impressions of them.

1. Divide the following characters into two lists: in one list place those characters you think Steinbeck intends us to like; in the other, list those characters Steinbeck means us to dislike.

- LENNIE and GEORGE -
THE MAIN CHARACTERS. MIGRANT WORKERS WHO FIND WORK ON THE RANCH.

CANDY and CANDY'S DOG
'SWAMPER' WHO CLEANS OUT THE BUNK-HOUSE.

- SLIM -
HEAD OF ONE OF THE 'GRAIN TEAMS'.

- CROOKS -
STABLE-HAND WHO MENDS HARNESSES AND OTHER RANCH EQUIPMENT.

- CARLSON and WHIT -
WORKERS ON THE RANCH.

CURLEY and CURLEY'S WIFE
BOSS' SON AND HIS WIFE, RECENTLY MARRIED. HE IS A LIGHTWEIGHT BOXER.

2. Compare your list with a friend's list. Were there any characters you found difficult to place?

3. The ranch boss appears very briefly in the story. However, the way he speaks and behaves tells us a little bit about the relationship between employer and worker. Make brief notes saying how he is regarded by the men (see Candy's comments at the beginning of Chapter 2) and the impression you get of him.

Geography and biography

- To explore how a writer's life can sometimes provide insights into his or her work.

1. Read the following notes on John Steinbeck's life and works, and look at the map.

John Steinbeck

Born in 1902 in Salinas, California.

His first well-known novel, *Tortilla Flat* (1935) is about a group of aimless men and women living near Monterey, and his early novel *In Dubious Battle (1936)* concerns a group of migrant fruit-pickers.

His great novel, *The Grapes of Wrath* (1939) tells the story of a family travelling from Oklahoma to California in search of the 'land of plenty' after they suffer in the Great Depression – and failing to find it.

Cannery Row (1945) takes place in Monterey, and *The Pearl* (1947) tells the story of a poor Mexican family who find a precious stone that they think will be their salvation, but which proves to be their destruction.

Another of his well-known novels, *East of Eden* (1952) is set in the Salinas valley.

Other novels are set away from the west coast of America, but when Steinbeck died in 1968 it was for the works above that he was best remembered.

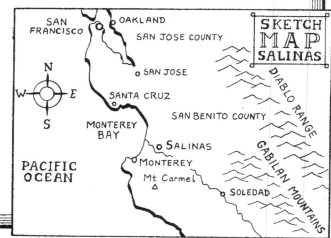

2. In pairs, discuss what evidence there is that John Steinbeck wrote about real places and/or places he knew in his novels?

3. Write down any connections you can see between *Of Mice and Men* and any of the novels mentioned above.

The Great Depression

FOCUS

- To consider whether *Of Mice and Men* can be related to the social conditions of the time in which it was written.

1. Read this passage that describes some of the key events of the 1920s and 1930s.

The phrase 'Roaring Twenties' has been used to describe the decade when America believed itself to be powerful, successful and wealthy. The truth was, things were not as good as they seemed; there was a big gap between rich and poor and there were problem areas such as agriculture.

In fact, in October 1929 share prices in New York fell dramatically. It is estimated that 26 billion dollars of investors' money was lost by the end of the month. This meant that all over the country companies went out of business, people lost their savings and those who had borrowed heavily had to sell their homes. The country was plunged into recession. This period is often referred to as the 'Great Depression'.

By 1933 about 30 percent of the workforce was unemployed. Many Americans simply took to the road to find work, some taking their whole family with them, others setting off on their own. Where they could find work wages were often low, and the conditions hard.

Although life was difficult, Hollywood continued to make glamorous films, such as *Gone with the Wind* (1939). Those that could afford the tickets were able to forget, briefly, the worries of life, but things did not really improve until many years later, in post-war America.

2. Discuss the following in pairs.
   a. What were the 1920s called in America?
   b. What event triggered the Great Depression?

3. Write down what aspects of the book show that the writer was aware of what was happening to ordinary working people.

4. Reread the section in Chapter 5 when Curley's wife tells Lennie about the chance she had to get into the movies. Write a brief summary of what stopped her and what happened as a result.

5. The Great Depression provides part of the backdrop to *Of Mice and Men* but is not central to the story, unlike in *The Grapes of Wrath*. Find out what happens in *The Grapes of Wrath*. A summary of the events will be enough.

Who says?

FOCUS

- To identify the speakers of a number of quotations and identify the order in which they appear in the novel.

Said by_____

To _____

1. The following lines are all spoken by characters at various stages of the novel. Identify the speaker of each and who is being spoken to.

a. "When they can me here I wisht somebody'd shoot me."

Said by_____

To _____

c. "You gonna get me in trouble jus' like George says you will."

Said by_____

To _____

b. "I could get along so easy and nice if I didn't have you on my tail."

Said by_____

To _____

d. "If you want me to, I'll put the old devil out of his misery right now and get it over with."

e. "I could get you strung up on a tree so easy it ain't even funny."

Said by_____

To _____

About _____

Said by_____

To _____

f. "I tell you I ain't used to livin' like this. I coulda made somethin' of myself."

2. Check your answers with a partner.

3. Number the quotations above in the order in which they appear in the text.

4. Select five quotations of your own, spoken by different characters, and test your partner's knowledge on who says them and where they appear in the novel.

First pages

- To explore the relevance and importance of the opening pages of *Of Mice and Men*.

Statement

- The first few pages of a novel can tell us a great deal about the story as a whole. To what extent is this true of *Of Mice and Men*?

1. Explore to what extent this is true, first by reading this information about the first five to six pages. The writer:

   - describes real geographical locations using the present tense

   - describes the landscape and setting

   - introduces us to the two main characters

   - shows us the ways in which the two main characters speak

   - tells us a little about what has already happened before the novel begins

   - tells us a little about what is about to happen in Chapter 2.

Example

'A few miles south of Soledad, the Salinas River drops in close to the hill-side bank and runs deep and green.'
(Page 1) Mentions real geographical locations.

2. On your own, copy out phrases or sentences from the first five to six pages that support the above statement. These are **quotations** and should be placed inside inverted commas. Write the relevant page number alongside each quotation together with the appropriate point from the list in Question 1.

3. Now complete the following sentence.

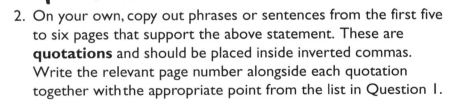

   John Steinbeck describes real geographical locations and uses the present tense to do so on the first two pages because he wants to _____

   _____

   _____

4. The way characters behave when they first appear can provide a clue to their personalities. Read once again the way Lennie imitates George when they stop by the pool and the conversation that follows. What clues does this give us about Lennie, and the men's relationship?

A tell-tale title

FOCUS

- To explore the relevance of the title of *Of Mice and Men*.

Introduction

A good title can give us the 'flavour' of the story as a whole and even add to our understanding of it. *Of Mice and Men* takes its title from the Robert Burns poem 'To a Mouse'. Burns describes turning a mouse's nest over with his plough and ruining her carefully built home.

1. Read the verse from 'To a Mouse.'

But Mousie, thou art no thy lane,
In proving foresight may be vain:
The best laid schemes o' mice an' men
Gang aft agley,
An' lea'e us nought but grief an' pain,
For promis'd joy!

Word Bank
lane – lone/alone
gang – go
aft – often
agley – askew/wrong

2. Write a standard English translation of the above verse.

3. Fill in the chart below by listing the dreams, hopes or schemes the characters have, and how they go wrong. The first one has been done for you.

Character	Dream or scheme	What happens
Crooks	Helping on the farm	Lennie dies, so no farm
Candy		
George		
Lennie		
Curley's wife		

4. For what other reason is the title particularly appropriate for the story?

5. Could *Of Mice and Men* have an alternative title? Invent three of your own.

Chapter 1

FOCUS

- To identify and explain four scenes from Chapter 1.

- Write a caption under each picture to explain what is happening.

1. _____

_____

2. _____

_____

3. _____

_____

4. _____

_____

Chapter 2

- To recognise key events in Chapter 2.

- Fill in the answers to these questions on Chapter 2.

1. Who is the first person to meet George and Lennie when they enter the bunk-house?

_____

2. Who appears wearing '... blue jean trousers, a flannel shirt, a black, unbuttoned vest and a black coat ... a soiled brown Stetson hat ... high-heeled boots and spurs to prove he was not a labouring man'?

_____

3. What made-up reason does George give the ranch boss for why he looks after Lennie?

_____

4. How does Curley behave towards Lennie and George when he comes into the bunk-house?

_____

5. How long has Curley been married?

_____

6. How is Curley's wife's voice described when she first speaks to George and Lennie?

_____

7. Whose '... authority was so great, that his word was taken on any subject, be it politics or love'?

_____

8. What is Carlson's reason for asking Slim about the puppies his dog has given birth to?

_____

9. Chapter 2 ends with the reappearance of one of the men. Who is he, and what does he want?

_____

Chapter 3

- To complete a summary of Chapter 3.

- Fill in the missing information in this summary of Chapter 3.

Chapter 3 begins with George telling _____ all about what happened in Weed to Lennie. He also explains how he and Lennie were both born in _____ and how George knew Lennie's Aunt _____ .

Lennie comes in, but George realises he is hiding the _____ he has been given. George makes him put it back.

Carlson persuades _____ that his dog is too old and should be put down. He takes it outside and shoots it, while the others try to play _____ .

Lennie returns from the barn and then _____ bursts in looking for his wife. He thinks _____ might be with her and leaves, followed by Whit and Carlson.

Candy offers to put his savings and retirement money into the farm Lennie and George have dreamed about. George says the farm will cost about _____ .

Curley and the others return. _____ warns Curley that he should look after his wife more. Curley picks a fight with Lennie.

Lennie refuses to fight back until _____ tells him to. Lennie grabs Curley's hand and crushes it.

Slim threatens Curley that if he tells his father what happened, they will tell everyone how Curley was beaten and humiliated by Lennie. Curley is to pretend he caught his hand in a _____ .

Chapter 4

FOCUS

- To exhibit knowledge of the conversations in Crooks' room.

- Complete the following paragraphs that describe the various conversations in Crooks' room.

Lennie and Crooks

Lennie comes into Crooks' room, saying he wants to look at his puppy. At first, Crooks tells him he is not wanted because ...

Candy, Lennie and Crooks

Candy comes in, looking for Lennie. He begins by complimenting Crooks on his room but Crooks answers sarcastically, mentioning ...

Curley's wife, Candy, Lennie and Crooks

Curley's wife enters, saying she's looking for Curley, then starts talking about her husband. She says that he is ...

George, Candy, Lennie and George

When George comes in, he reprimands Crooks for allowing Candy and Lennie to come in, then is cross when he realises that Lennie has ...

MODERN CLASSICS: *Of Mice and Men*

Chapter 5

FOCUS

● To identify the order, and write a summary, of events in Chapter 5.

1. These pictures represent what happens in Chapter 5. They are in the wrong order. Number them in sequence and then write a brief caption for each picture. For example, the caption for the first picture could be, 'Enter trouble'.

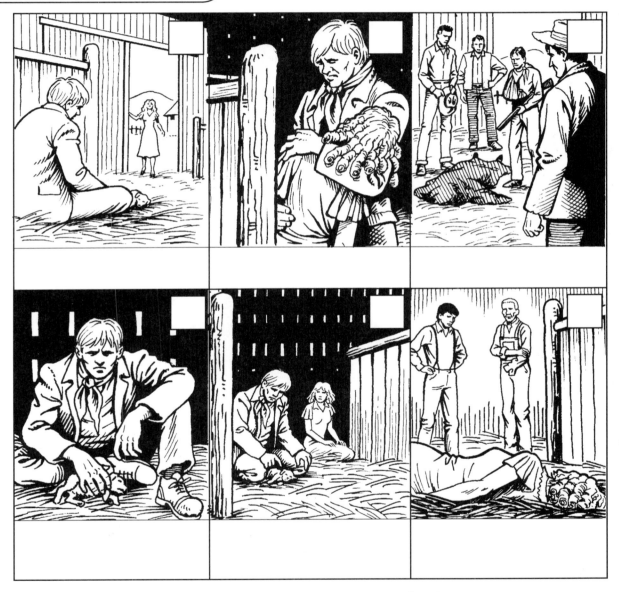

2. Write a summary of 150–200 words explaining what happens in the above pictures.

3. There are at least two other events that are not shown here. Who finds the body first? Who leaves so the others do not think he is involved in the killing? Draw two further pictures to show these events and decide where they would fit into the sequence.

Chapter 6

FOCUS

● To revise the events at the pool.

1. Reread Chapter 6 and then write answers to the questions below.

2. Lennie has two conversations with himself before George arrives. The first is with Aunt Clara. What does she look like and what does she tell Lennie?

3. Lennie's second conversation is even stranger. Who or what speaks to him this time? What effect does the conversation have on Lennie?

4. When George finally catches up with Lennie, Lennie expects – and perhaps wants George – to 'give him hell', almost as a form of comfort. George does so, dutifully, but what does the way he speaks tell us about his real feelings? Read this example.

> He said woodenly, "If I was alone I could live so easy." His voice was monotonous, had no emphasis. "I could get a job an' not have no mess." He stopped.
>
> "Go on," said Lennie ...

MODERN CLASSICS: *Of Mice and Men*

George

- To write a detailed character study of George.

1. Record your ideas about George under the following headings.

Your impression of him

Key quotations that describe him (said by him, the writer or other characters)

His involvement in the story: what he does and what happens to him

2. Now, using your notes, write about George's character and his importance to the story, using quotations and referring closely to his part in the events that occur.

Lennie

- To write a detailed character study of Lennie.

1. Record your ideas about Lennie under the following headings.

Your impression of him

Key quotations that describe him (said by him, the writer or other characters)

His involvement in the story: what he does and what happens to him

2. Now, using your notes, write about Lennie's character and his importance to the story, using quotations and referring closely to his part in the events that occur.

Slim

● To write a detailed character study of Slim.

1. Record your ideas about Slim under the following headings.

Your impression of him

Key quotations that describe him (said by him, the writer or other characters)

His involvement in the story: what he does and what happens to him

2. Now, using your notes, write about Slim's character and his importance to the story, using quotations and referring closely to his part in the events that occur.

Candy

● To write a detailed character study of Candy.

1. Record your ideas about Candy under the following headings.

Your impression of him

Key quotations that describe him (said by him, the writer or other characters)

His involvement in the story: what he does and what happens to him

2. Now, using your notes, write about Candy's character and his importance to the story, using quotations and referring closely to his part in the events that occur.

Curley

- To write a detailed character study of Curley.

1. Record your ideas about Curley under the following headings.

Your impression of him

Key quotations that describe him (said by him, the writer or other characters)

His involvement in the story: what he does and what happens to him

---

2. Now, using your notes, write about Curley's character and his importance to the story, using quotations and referring closely to his part in the events that occur.

Curley's wife

- To write a detailed character study of Curley's wife.

1. Record your ideas about Curley's wife under the following headings.

Your impression of her

Key quotations that describe her (said by her, the writer or other characters)

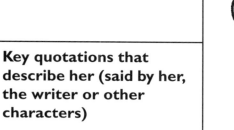

Her involvement in the story: what she does and what happens to her

2. Now, using your notes, write about Curley's wife's character and her importance to the story, using quotations and referring closely to her part in the events that occur.

Crooks

- To write a detailed character study of Crooks.

1. Record your ideas about Crooks under the following headings.

Your impression of him

Key quotations that describe him (said by him, the writer or other characters)

His involvement in the story: what he does and what happens to him

---

2. Now, using your notes, write about Crooks' character and his importance to the story, using quotations and referring closely to his part in the events that occur.

Minor characters

FOCUS

- To research the three minor characters in *Of Mice and Men*.

- Record your ideas about the following characters under the headings provided.

Your impression of him	Carlson	One key quotation about him from the novel

Your impression of him	Whit	One key quotation about him from the novel

Your impression of him	The ranch boss	One key quotation about him from the novel

MODERN CLASSICS: *Of Mice and Men*   © Folens (copiable page)

Steinbeck's language – dialect

FOCUS

- To identify the speakers of key quotations and rewrite them in standard English.

Introduction

John Steinbeck uses the language that he believes real people would have used in this part of America, living this way of life. Understanding what they are saying is important to understanding their behaviour.

- The following quotations are taken from conversations in Chapter 3. Identify who is speaking in each case and rewrite each in standard English.

1. Speaker: _____   Your version: _____

"I ain't done nothing, George. Slim says I better not pet them pups so much for a while. Slim says it ain't good for them; so I come right in. I been good, George."

2. Speaker: _____   Your version: _____

"She's gonna make a mess. They's gonna be a bad mess. She's a jail-bait all set on a trigger."

3. Speaker: _____   Your version: _____

"Hardly none of the guys ever travel together. I hardly never seen two guys travel together. You know how the hands are, they just come in and get their bunk and work a month, and then they quit and go out alone."

4. Speaker: _____   Your version: _____

"I ought to of shot that dog myself, George. I shouldn't ought to of let no stranger shoot my dog."

5. Speaker: _____   Your version: _____

"You tried to throw a scare into Slim, 'an you couldn't make it stick. Slim throwed a scare into you. You're yella as a frog belly ..."

Steinbeck's language – character

FOCUS

- To explore two examples of Steinbeck's language style.

Introduction

Writers use language in a variety of ways in order to make characters and situations come alive.

1. Here are some descriptions of Lennie taken from Chapter 1. Write down the overall impression they create of him.

'... he walked heavily, dragging his feet a little, the way a bear drags his paws.'

'(he) ... drank with long gulps, snorting into the water like a horse.'

'Lennie dabbled his big paw in the water ...'

'Lennie lumbered to his feet ...'

'Lennie crawled slowly and cautiously around the fire ...'

Some of the key words in the above descriptions are verbs and they give a clear and specific picture of Lennie's movements. For example: '**dragging** his feet', '**snorting** into the water', '**dabbled** his big paw', '**lumbered** to his feet'.

2. The images above give one view of Lennie, but another is given through the way Steinbeck makes his behaviour and speech almost like a child's. For example, in the way he describes Lennie imitating and looking up to George.

   He pushed himself back, drew up his knees, embraced them, looked over to George to see whether he had it just right. He pulled his hat down a little more over his eyes, the way George's hat was.

3. On your own, work through the whole of Chapter 1 and write down as many examples as you can of individual words, phrases or sentences that suggest Lennie is like a child.

MODERN CLASSICS: *Of Mice and Men*

Steinbeck at the movies

FOCUS

- To consider some issues involved in adapting *Of Mice and Men*, and compare the book and film versions.

Introduction

Most great novels have been adapted for the cinema – some have been made into films several times. *Of Mice and Men* has been made into a film twice. First, in 1939 in black and white, with Lon Chaney Junior as Lennie, and then in colour in 1992 with John Malkovich taking the same role.

John Steinbeck
Of Mice and
Men

1. In pairs, discuss:

   a. Why is *Of Mice and Men* a relatively straightforward film to adapt?
   b. What problems, if any, would the adaptation of the book present?

2. In the 1992 version of the film, many conversations have been edited and new scenes added. We see:

   - the men working in the fields and Lennie's enormous strength
   - a scene in which Curley's wife seems to be flirting with George on his own.

   a. How is the evidence of Lennie's strength and fast work rate shown in the novel? (See the beginning of Chapter 3.)
   b. Why do you think the director of the 1992 film felt the need to introduce an extra scene between Curley's wife and George?

3. Here are three possible ways that a new version of the film might begin. Choose the one you think would make the best beginning and write a full explanation of your reasons, also saying why you rejected the others.

   a. The film begins with Lennie and George hiding in an irrigation ditch after the incident at Weed.
   b. The film begins with the two men entering the bunk-house. It misses out the conversation between Lennie and George at the pool.
   c. The film begins with George sitting behind Lennie, holding the gun to his head.

Lennie's dream

- To focus on some of the aspects of Lennie and George's dream.

Introduction
Dreams and hopes are central to the novel, especially Lennie and George's dream of living off 'the fatta the lan'.

1. Look at the picture below, which is a visual representation of Lennie's and George's dream.

2. Copy and complete the following table, listing the various elements of the dream, as told by George in Chapter 3. The picture above may help.

Buildings	Fruit and vegetables	Meat	Crops	Animals

3. What is it that excites Lennie most about the plan?

4. Is George as committed to the plan as Lennie? Give reasons for your answers.

5. Make notes on:

   a. Who else expresses interest in the plan
   b. Why they are interested
   c. What different things they offer George and Lennie

Friendship

Introduction

The relationship between Lennie and George is central to the story – but can we really call it a friendship? At the beginning of Chapter 3 Slim says to George, ' "Funny how you an' him string along together." '

1. In pairs, discuss what makes a good friendship and how you can tell when two people are good friends.

2. On your own, reread Chapter 3 until the point when Lennie enters the bunk-house. In your own words list five reasons why George tells Slim he and Lennie stay together.

   a. _____

   _____

   b. _____

   _____

   c. _____

   _____

d. _____

_____

e. _____

_____

3. The life on the ranch ought to be one where friendships are easy, but with the exception of Lennie and George no one has someone they can strictly call a friend. Even Curley's wife does not like her husband. Once Lennie is dead, is there anyone George can be friends with?

4. Take each character, except Curley's wife, and write a paragraph on each, saying how likely it is that George will see him as a friend if he remains on the ranch.

Motives

- To understand why George, Candy, Curley and Curley's wife behave as they do.

- In each of the following cases, imagine you are the named character and then write your answer to each of the questions. Use the information in brackets to help you.

1. **Question:** Why did you decide to travel with Lennie?
(Reread George's conversation with Slim at the beginning of Chapter 3.)

George: _____

_____

_____

2. **Question:** Why did you not try to stop Carlson from shooting your dog?
(Think about Carlson's character and Candy's age.)

Candy: _____

_____

_____

3. **Question:** Why did you pick on Lennie when you came back into the bunk-house with Slim and Carlson in Chapter 3?
(Reread the section starting, 'The door opened. Slim came in ...' towards the end of Chapter 3. Think about the way Slim and Carlson talk to Curley.)

Curley: _____

_____

_____

4. **Question:** Why did you go to see Lennie in the barn when you knew his strength and what your husband would think?
(Think about what Curley's wife says about her life throughout the book.)

Curley's wife: _____

_____

_____

Questions

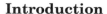

FOCUS

- To put yourself in the role of the local lawman or law woman and explore the circumstances of Lennie's death.

Introduction

Imagine you are the local lawman or law woman and you are called to the scene of Lennie's death. You know nothing other than what you see and what you are told.

1. Describe the scene that you find at the pool.

   a. Who is there?
   b. What do you see?
   c. What are your first impressions?

2. You have time to interview George, Curley and Candy. Write down two questions you would ask each character.

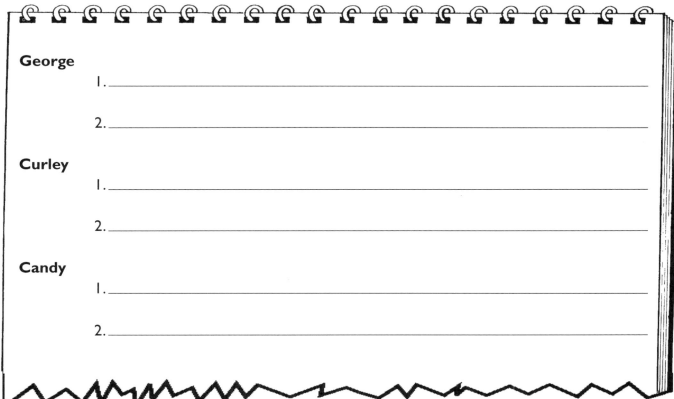

George

1. _____

2. _____

Curley

1. _____

2. _____

Candy

1. _____

2. _____

3. Now exchange your sheet of questions with a partner. He/she must write out full answers to your questions and you must answer his/hers. Try to put yourself in the characters' shoes when you answer your partner's questions.

Incident in Weed

- To rewrite a newspaper report on the incident in Weed.

1. The following is a possible newspaper account of what happened in Weed before the novel began. Some of the names are made up, but the facts are correct. Read the report.

The Weed Chronicle

GIRL FRAMES SIMPLETON

Yesterday afternoon local girl, Suzie Murphy, accused a simple-minded travelling worker, a Mr Lennie Small, who was passing through Weed with his companion, George Milton, of having tried to assault her in broad daylight. Mr Small, a very large man of below average intelligence, had merely complimented her on her attire and had briefly touched her red dress, when she called out in panic that she was being attacked. Local people, including several lawmen, rushed to the scene, by which time the accused man had taken off, in fear of his life. A witness to yesterday's events, who wished to remain nameless, said, "It has come to a pretty pass, when two decent men, without work, are pursued by a lynch-mob before the true facts of the situation have been established. I am truly ashamed to be a citizen of Weed."

The two men are now reported to have left the area, although local lawmen are searching irrigation ditches following a reported sighting last night of two men answering their description.

2. It is highly unlikely that the local paper would, in fact, have reported the events in this way. Rewrite the report so that the newspaper appears sympathetic to the girl. You will need to:

– remove phrases such as 'lynch-mob'
– have a different witness statement
– refer to Lennie and George in less complimentary ways.

A marriage made in hell

FOCUS

- To consider the relationship between Curley and his wife?

Introduction

Curley's wife speaks about her husband in less than favourable terms. She says, ' "Swell guy, ain't he? Spends all his time sayin' what he's gonna do to guys he don't like, and he don't like nobody. Think I'm gonna stay in that two-by-four house ... ?" '

1. Imagine that after Curley's wife has been in Crooks' room (Chapter 3), she returns to the house and stays up until Curley comes back from town (possibly having spent his money on other women). When he returns they talk. Write the script of their conversation below. You could start with the following.

Remember:
- Curley's temper
- Curley's wife's ambitions
- Curley's jealousy
- the injury to Curley's hand and his wife's suspicions.

Curley's wife:	Where you been? As if I don't know.
Curley:	Ain't a guy allowed out? 'Tain't no business of yours.
Curley's wife:	'Tis my business if you won't let me out. Think I came here to wait 'roun' for you?

2. There are a large number of other conversations that must take place, but which we never hear in the story. Choose one of the following conversations and write the script.
   - Ranch boss and Curley – Curley explaining what happened to his hand.
   - Slim and Curley – Curley questioning Slim about his wife's interest in him.
   - Curley's wife and Slim – Curley's wife flirting with Slim.

MODERN CLASSICS: *Of Mice and Men*

Mental handicap

FOCUS

- To explore whether Lennie is really to blame for his actions.

Introduction
In Chapter 3 Slim says, ' "He's a nice fella, ... Guy don't need no sense to be a nice fella. Seems to me sometimes it jus' works the other way around. Take a real smart guy and he ain't hardly ever a nice fella." ' But, is Lennie really a 'nice fella'?

1. In pairs, discuss which of the following things can be said to be Lennie's fault.

   – He scares a girl in Weed.
   – He crushes Curley's hand.
   – He kills the puppy he has been given.
   – He kills Curley's wife.

2. Now read the following extract from Chapter 5, which occurs shortly after Lennie has killed Curley's wife.

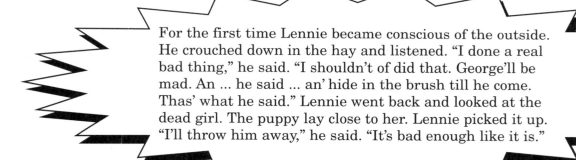

For the first time Lennie became conscious of the outside. He crouched down in the hay and listened. "I done a real bad thing," he said. "I shouldn't of did that. George'll be mad. An ... he said ... an' hide in the brush till he come. Thas' what he said." Lennie went back and looked at the dead girl. The puppy lay close to her. Lennie picked it up. "I'll throw him away," he said. "It's bad enough like it is."

3. Write down the answers to the following questions.

   a. Does Lennie feel any guilt for what he has done?
   b. What line shows that Lennie's judgement of the situation is at best childlike and at worst severely impaired?

4. George says early on that a horse kicked Lennie in the head, which seems to be a convenient lie. Whatever is the cause of his slowness, it is not Lennie's fault, and the ending is a tragedy for him and George. Write a short piece saying how you think Lennie would be treated if he committed a similar act today. Can you be sure he would be treated more humanely?

MODERN CLASSICS: *Of Mice and Men*

The issue of race

- To investigate the characters' attitude towards Crooks and the issue of race.

Introduction
Of Mice and Men is not a story about race yet it has a part to play in the story and the characters' attitudes to it partly shape our views of them.

1. Read the following extract from Chapter 4, in which Crooks is speaking to Curley's wife.

"I had enough," he said coldly. "You got no rights comin' in a coloured man's room. You got no rights messing around in here at all. Now you jus' get out, an' get out quick. If you don't, I'm gonna ast the boss not to ever let you come in the barn no more."

She turned to him in scorn. "Listen, Nigger," she said. "You know what I can do if you open your trap?"

Crooks stared hopelessly at her, and then he sat down on his bunk and drew into himself.

She closed on him. "You know what I could do?" Crooks seemed to grow smaller, and he pressed himself against the wall. "Yes, ma'am."

"Well, you keep your place then, Nigger. I could get you strung up on a tree so easy it ain't even funny."

Crooks had reduced himself to nothing. There was no personality, no ego – nothing to arouse either like or dislike. He said, "Yes, ma'am," and his voice was toneless.

2. Crooks is treated with a certain respect by some on the ranch, but he is still viewed by others, such as Curley and Carlson, as a semi-slave. Curley's wife goes further. Discuss with a partner how she threatens him and the effect this threat has on Crooks.

3. After Curley's wife leaves, Crooks says, ' "Maybe you guys better go." ' Write down what Candy says in reply and what this tells us about the type of person Candy is.

4. In one way, Curley's wife has something in common with Lennie, Candy and Crooks – they are all outsiders. Write a paragraph on each of the four, explaining in what ways this is true.

Using quotations

Introduction

As in any text that is being studied, it is important to select quotations carefully. You use quotations when it is necessary to provide evidence of the **actual words** used by the writer, in order to support a point you are making.

Advice

1. **Integrating quotations**

   Point: George is in a form of shock as a result of shooting Lennie.

   Evidence: 'George's voice was almost a whisper.'

   In an essay you would merge the quotation and the previous sentence into one sentence as follows.

   George is clearly shaken by what he has had to do, as the writer mentions that his **'voice was almost a whisper.'** (Chapter 6)

   You will notice that the quotation is not the full sentence used by the writer. The first word 'George's' has been dropped so that the point made and the quotation merge together easily, in one sentence.

2. **Full quotations**

   Often, you may wish to use a longer quotation and use it in its entirety. On these occasions it makes sense to introduce the quotation in a more general sense and then leave a line space. For example:

   After George has gone and left Candy alone with the body of Curley's wife, Candy realises the dream is over.

   'His eyes blinded with tears and he turned and went weakly out of the barn, and he rubbed his bristly whiskers with his wrist stump.' (Chapter 5)

   After the quotation itself, the words are 'picked over' and a number are selected for further, more detailed comment.

   The fact that Candy is crying, the fact that he is moving 'weakly', and the writer's reminder of his disability – his 'wrist-stump' all serve to heighten the sense of tragedy.

● Look at the passage in Chapter 5 when Curley's wife is telling Lennie how she could have been in the movies. Choose a point to make about her. For example, she is disappointed, bitter, likes confiding ... , and then find quotations to integrate into your writing in the two ways shown above.

Curley's wife

FOCUS

- To write an essay about the fate of Curley's wife.

Essay title

'Curley's wife deserved her fate.' Do you agree?

Planning

- **Stage 1:** Check you understand the question and note the key words of the question. The first is noted for you:

  '**Curley's wife**'

- **Stage 2:** One of your key words is probably '**deserved**'. In order to consider how much Curley's wife deserved what happened to her you should read, and make judgements from, the indicated passages.

  First, read the section in Chapter 2 when Curley's wife comes into the bunk-house looking for Curley. (Pages 32–34). Notice the following key line.

  George says to Lennie: "I seen 'em poison before, but I never seen no piece of jail-bait worse than her. You leave her be."

  Read the section in Chapter 4 when she comes into Crooks' place – the harness room. (Pages 81–86). Notice the following key lines.

  She says to Candy: "Think I don't like to talk to somebody ever, once in a while? Think I like to stick in that house alla time?

  She says to Crooks: "I could get you strung up on a tree so easy it ain't even funny."

  Now, read the section in Chapter 5 when she finds Lennie in the barn. (Pages 91–96). Notice the following key lines.

  She says to Lennie: "I get lonely … .You can talk to people, but I can't talk to nobody but Curley. Else he gets mad."

  "I coulda made somethin' of myself."

  "… you're a kinda nice fella. Jus' like a big baby."

- **Stage 3:** Now, make a list under two headings:
  1. Reasons to dislike her.   2. Reasons to feel sorry for her.

- Now, write your essay.

Tragedy revealed

FOCUS

- To compare and contrast the roles of Lennie and George.

 Essay title

'The real tragedy of the story is not what happens to Lennie, but what happens to George.' Discuss.

Planning

- **Stage 1:** In order to understand the title you need to answer the following question first. What is a tragedy?

  In Shakespeare's day this tended to mean an important character or hero who was brought down by a weakness.

  In pairs, discuss whether George has a weakness? If so, what is it?

- **Stage 2:** You now need to trace exactly what happens to George in the story. On your own, copy and complete the table below. Lennie's experiences have already been filled in.

George	Lennie
	– Mistakenly accused of rape in Weed. – Relies on George to get him a job at the ranch. – Makes impression with his great strength when working. – Crushes Curley's fist in fight. – Accidentally kills puppy given to him by Slim. – Panics and kills Curley's wife. – Runs off and is found by George. – George before the others arrive.

- **Stage 3:** Finally, you need evidence to show how George has suffered.

  1. Find and write down a quotation from Chapter 1 that tells us what George says he has given up to look after Lennie.

  2. Find and write down a quotation or any individual words from the end of the book that suggest what George feels when he kills Lennie.

- Now, write your essay using the notes you have compiled. Half the essay should be on what happens to George and the other half on what happens to Lennie. You should then draw your conclusions.

A modern-day fable

FOCUS

- To write an essay tracing the shape and form of the story in terms of its basic ingredients.

Essay title

Of Mice and Men has been called a simple, modern fable. In what ways is this true?

Planning

- **Stage 1:** A fable is usually considered to mean a short, simple tale in which one character learns a lesson from an experience he or she undergoes. In pairs, discuss any examples of fables you know (e.g. 'The Hare and the Tortoise'). Discuss what happens in them.

- **Stage 2:** Is *Of Mice and Men* a **simple** tale? Tick either **yes** or **no** for the questions in the table below.

	Yes	No
1. Does the story jump around from time to time, from present to past?		
2. Does it take place in lots of different places or in geographically distant places around the world.		
3. Does it have a large number of characters?		
4. Does it tell lots of different stories.		

- **Stage 3:** Characters in fables usually get 'taught a lesson' because of something they have done wrong. What lesson, if any, does George or any other character learn?

- **Stage 4:** Fables are generally rounded off quite neatly, and seem complete. Write a paragraph saying in what way the ending of *Of Mice and Men* is neat. (Think about where the story begins.)

- Now, write your essay. It will be helpful to refer to the proverb suggested by the title (i.e. 'The best laid schemes o' mice an' men Gang aft agley. An' lea'e us nought but grief an' pain, For promis'd joy!') as many fables end with proverbs.

The death of Candy's dog

- To identify key elements of Steinbeck's language style.

1. The following passage describes the moment when Carlson takes Candy's dog out of the bunk-house to shoot it.
a. Go through the text and circle all the words referring to sounds and 'silence'
b. Then go through and underline lines that contain close detail about handling the cards
c. Finally, in a different colour, underline the one spoken sentence that refers directly to the shooting of the dog.

It was silent outside. Carlson's footsteps died away. The silence came into the room. And the silence lasted.

George chuckled, "I bet Lennie's right out there in the barn with his pup. He won't want to come in here no more now he's got a pup."

Slim said, "Candy, you can have any one of them pups you want."

Candy did not answer. The silence fell on the room again. It came out of the night and invaded the room. George said, "Anybody like to play a little euchre?"

"I'll play out a few with you," said Whit.

They took places opposite each other at the table under the light, but George did not shuffle the cards. He rippled the edge of the deck nervously, and the little snapping noise drew the eyes of all the men in the room, so he stopped doing it. The silence fell on the room again. A minute passed, and another minute. Candy lay still, staring at the ceiling. Slim gazed at him for a moment and then looked down at his hands; he subdued one hand with the other, and held it down. There came a little gnawing sound from under the floor and all the men looked down toward it gratefully. Only Candy continued to stare at the ceiling.

"Sounds like there was a rat under there," said George. "We ought to get a trap down there."

Whit broke out, "What the hell's takin' him so long? Lay out some cards, why don't you? We ain't gonna get no euchre played this way."

George brought the cards together tightly and studied the backs of them. The silence was in the room again.

A shot sounded in the distance. The men looked quickly at the old man. Every head turned toward him.

For a moment he continued to stare at the ceiling. Then he rolled slowly over and faced the wall and lay silent.

The death of Candy's dog (continued)

FOCUS

- Use identified features in detailed analytical writing.

Essay title

How does John Steinbeck convey the tension of the situation in the card-playing passage of Chapter 3?

Planning

- **Stage 1:** Reread the passage on the previous sheet and look again at the lines and words you have underlined and circled.

- **Stage 2:** Four key elements enable the writer to convey tension:

  > - the way the passing of time is indicated
  > - the repetition of words referring to 'silence' and various sounds
  > - the way the writer uses dialogue to convey the inability of the characters to communicate their feelings
  > - the writer's attention to minute detail, particularly the movement of the men.

On your own, go through the text again and write a paragraph on each of the four elements using the lines above as starter sentences.

Example
The writer conveys tension in the way the passing of time is indicated. For example, he describes ...

- **Stage 3:** Add a further paragraph or two detailing any other elements that have not been mentioned, such as the length of the sentences, use of verbs etc.

- Now, write your essay.

Exam passage I

● Read this passage carefully and then answer all questions that follow it.

Crooks, the negro stable buck, had his bunk in the harness room; a little shed that leaned off the wall of the barn. On one side of the little room there was a square four-paned window, and, on the other, a narrow plank door leading into the barn. Crooks' bunk was a long box filled with straw, on which his blankets were flung. On the wall by the window there were pegs on which hung broken harness in process of being mended, strips of new leather; and under the window itself a little bench for leather-working tools, curved knives and needles and ball of linen thread, and a small hand riveter. On pegs were also pieces of harness, a split collar with the horsehair stuffing sticking out, a broken hame, and a trace chain with its leather covering split. Crooks had his apple-box over his bunk, and in it a range of medicine bottles, both for himself and for the horses. There were cans of saddle soap and a drippy can of tar with its paint-brush sticking over the edge. And scattered about the floor were a number of personal possessions; for, being alone, Crooks could leave his things about, and being a stable buck and a cripple, <u>he was more permanent than the other men</u>, and he had accumulated more possessions than he could carry on his back.

Crooks possessed several pairs of shoes, a pair of rubber boots, a big alarm clock and a single-barrelled shotgun. And he had books, too; a tattered dictionary and a mauled copy of the California civil code for 1905. There were battered magazines and a few dirty books on a special shelf over his bunk. A pair of large gold-rimmed spectacles hung from a nail on the wall above his bed.

This room was swept and fairly neat, for Crooks was a proud, aloof man. He kept his distance and demanded that other people kept theirs. His body was bent over to the left by his crooked spine, and his eyes lay deep in his head, and because of their depth seemed to glitter with intensity. His lean face was lined with deep black wrinkles, and he had thin, pain-tightened lips which were lighter than his face.

Exam passage 1 (continued)

These questions are based on the passage.

1. Look at the underlined section of the text. Explain in detail how Crooks is different from most of the other men on the ranch.

2. In your own words, describe the room Crooks lives in — what its purpose is and what it suggests about the writer's knowledge.

_____

_____

_____

_____

_____

_____

_____

These questions are based on the text as a whole.

3. What evidence is there from the rest of the Chapter or the novel as a whole that Crooks 'kept his distance and demanded that other people kept theirs'?

_____

_____

_____

_____

4. Select one character from the novel who you think is most like Crooks or who Crooks would get along with best. Support your answer with close reference to what happens in the book and what Crooks says and does.

_____

_____

_____

_____

Exam passage 2

Read this passage carefully and then answer the question that follows.

And George raised the gun and steadied it, and he brought the muzzle of it close to the back of Lennie's head. The hand shook violently, but his face set and his hand steadied. He pulled the trigger. The crash of the shot rolled up the hills and rolled down again. Lennie jarred, and then settled slowly forward to the sand, and he lay without quivering.

George shivered and looked at the gun, and then he threw it from him, back up on the bank, near the pile of old ashes.

The brush seemed filled with cries and the sound of running feet. Slim's voice shouted, "George. Where you at, George?"

But George sat stiffly on the bank and looked at his right hand that had thrown the gun away. The group burst into the clearing, and Curley was ahead. He saw Lennie lying on the sand. "Got him, by God." He went over and looked down at Lennie, and then he looked back at George. "Right in the back of the head," he said softly.

Slim came directly to George and sat down beside him, sat very close to him. "Never you mind," said Slim. "A guy got to sometimes."

1. Imagine you are George. Write about how you feel and what you are thinking about as Slim speaks to you. You should consider the following in your planning.

   - What you have just done and whether it was justified.
   - Your feelings about Lennie.
   - Your position at the ranch and what the future holds.
   - How you feel about the other characters' behaviour.
   - The language you use.

MODERN CLASSICS: *Of Mice and Men*

Exam passage 2 (continued)

Planning

You may wish to use the headings below for your notes.

What you have just done and whether it was justified.

Your feelings about Lennie.

Your position at the ranch and what the future holds.

How you feel about the other characters' behaviour.

The language you use.

Final check

Go through your finished work and check the following. Tick each box when you have done so.

● Have you written out quotations accurately? ☐

● Have you spelled character names and place names correctly? ☐

● Are your sentences clear (do you need more full stops or connectives)? ☐

● Did you consider all the aspects you were supposed to? ☐

Selected answers

The whole story (Page 6)

1. c, d, j, f, a, g, b, i, e, h

Who says? (Page 10)

1. a. Candy to George and Lennie
   b. George to Lennie
   c. Lennie to Curley's wife
   d. Carlson to Candy about Candy's dog
   e. Curley's wife to Crooks
   f. Curley's wife to Lennie

2. b, e, a, d, f, c

Chapter 2 (Page 14)

1. Candy
2. Ranch boss
3. Horse kicked him in the head
4. Aggressive, suspicious
5. Two weeks
6. 'Nasal, brittle quality'
7. Slim
8. Carlson wants to get rid of Candy's dog and offers a puppy as a replacement
9. Curley, looking for his wife

Chapter 3 (Page 15)

Slim, Auburn, Clara, puppy, Candy, cards (euchre), Curley, Slim, 600 bucks, Slim, George, machine

Chapter 5 (Page 17)

1. 4, 1, 5, 2, 6, 3

3. Candy finds the body first. George is the one who leaves.

Friendship (Page 31)

2. Reasons for George travelling with Lennie:
   - says they are not so different – he (George) is not 'so bright'
   - they were born in the same town
   - he knew Lennie's Aunt Clara – when she died, it was natural for Lennie to tag along with him
   - guilt perhaps (George used to mistreat him, until the day he nearly drowned)
   - George himself has no family.